Caring *for a* Loved One *with* Cancer

HOPE
for the Heart

P.O. Box 7 • Dallas, TX • 75221

www.hopefortheheart.org

ISBN: 1-931734-04-6

To order other material related to this topic, contact
HOPE FOR THE HEART
P.O. Box 7 • Dallas, TX • 75221
or call toll-free
1.800.488.HOPE (4673)
www.hopefortheheart.org

Dear Friend,

What can you do when someone you love receives a devastating diagnosis? Do you have difficulty communicating your love and concern? Is there anything you can do to make a *real* difference?

Sometimes we don't know how to show we care. Sometimes we don't know how to express our feelings. Sometimes we don't know what others need from us.

During my bout with bilateral breast cancer, my friends and family were absolutely extraordinary. That's why I want to share the specific acts of love they did to help me face this unfriendly foe ... *the many deeds that made a real difference.*

My prayer is that this practical little book will help you express your heart and extend your care to any and every loved one who comes face-to-face with cancer ... or any critical illness.

Yours in the Lord's peace,

June

June Hunt

"The wise in heart are called discerning, and pleasant words promote instruction."

[PROVERBS 16:21]

Table *of* Contents

Practical Ways to Care for Your Loved One

Drive Your Loved One to the Doctor—If Cancer
   Could be the Diagnosis. 11
Don't Withhold Your Tears—They Tell That Your
   Heart Is Tender. 12
Gather a Group to Pray 13
Focus on Family Involvement 14
Give Time-tested Advice. 15
Offer Hands-on Help 16
Pen a Meaningful Poem. 17
Plan to Be Present 18
Give the Gift of Song. 19
Keep a Record of Remembrances. 20
Offer to Communicate Progress and Needs 21
Attend Doctor Appointments 22
Bring a Teddy Bear. 23
Lift the Spirit with Laughter 24
Pin Up Humorous Posters 25
Say You Can Stay at the Hospital. 26
Look for Little Tokens of Love 27
Make the First Move and Speak Wisely. 28
Offer to Be a "Go-fer". 30
Prepare a Rotation Plan for Primary Home Care 31
Bring Helpful Books, Videos, and Booklets 32
Ask Appropriate Questions 34
Invest Energy in the Internet. 37
Exert Initiative to Exercise. 39
Buy New Sleepwear 40
Offer Help for the Holidays 41
Fix Enough Food . . . for Caregivers Too. 42

Bring a Bouquet, Plant, or Helium Balloon 43
Seek Ways to Assuage Anxiety. 44
Help to Hunt for Head Covers 45
Encourage a "Journal for the Journey". 46
Make a Chart for Medications 47
Remind Gently of the Routine 48
Find Items Frequently Forgotten 49
Put Together a Scrapbook of Pictures 50
Fix Food That Helps with Healing 51
Help Your Loved One Live with Lymphedema. 52
Provide Comfy Clothes. 53
Be Sensitive about Special Occasions 54
Be Ready to Donate Blood 56
Convey God's Hope on Heart-shaped Cutouts 57
Consider a Cancer Support Group. 58
Plan a Regular Time to Pray 59
Consider a "Cancer Walk". 60
Give an Engraved Bracelet 61
Help Out at Home 62
Communicate Your Care with Cards. 63
Be Prepared to Help for the Long Haul 65
Accompany Your Loved One to Chemo 66
Don't Forget about the Children 70
Questions to Help Children 74
Tips for Temporary Trials 78
Discover the Important Don'ts 90
What Cancer Cannot Do 94
Do You Need Spiritual Healing? 96
Endnotes. 99
Selected Bibliography. 101

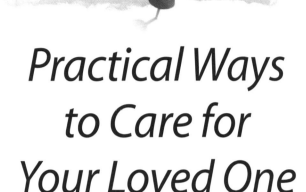

Practical Ways to Care for Your Loved One

Drive Your Loved One to the Doctor— If Cancer Could be the Diagnosis

1

Before the "C" diagnosis (C for cancer), Kay knew my initial concern.... I had a suspicion that a lump might be malignant. Kay said she was going with me for the sonogram. I said, "No, it isn't necessary." ... She said, "Yes, it is necessary." ... I said, "No." ... She said, "Yes!" ... I said, "No." ... She said, "Yes." Her persistence won out. And in retrospect, I was glad.

Kay knew that once a doctor gives the cancer diagnosis, the patient *remembers only 20%* of what is subsequently said. Following my examination, the radiologist walked into the room and said, *"I'm going to be straightforward with you. You do have a malignancy. You will have to have chemotherapy. You will lose your hair."* (What did the hair have to do with this!)

Then she proceeded to give me instructions. Instead of listening, I was thinking—*But I have to speak at a conference in Baltimore in two days and then speak on Crisis Counseling in New York City.* This was one month following September 11, 2001—the terrorist attacks on the Twin Towers. *I must go,* I thought, my mind whirling. At this point, I was hardly hearing a word the doctor said. So I interrupted her with my request, *"Excuse me, would you please go to the waiting room and ask Kay to join us?"*

Kay came in, took notes, and asked questions. Then we both went back to my home somewhat stunned. Throughout my entire ordeal, Kay has lived out the Scripture—again and again—*"There is a friend who sticks closer than a brother"* [PROVERBS 18:24].

(And yes, I did lead the conference in Baltimore ... and I did speak at the unforgettable conference in New York City.)

2 Don't Withhold Your Tears — They Tell That Your Heart Is Tender

When I first shared the news of my cancer with my closest friends, I was surprised to see them moved to tears. Actually, I was stunned! You see, years ago my father had said — incorrectly, of course — *"Tears are a sign of mental illness."* So, for years I trained myself not to cry, and even today I'm typically not prone to shed tears.

In truth, I had no idea that the tears of my friends would be so meaningful to me. I knew they stemmed from love and were a natural reaction to my unwanted illness and the uncertainty of its seriousness. They knew some of what lay ahead, a definite change of lifestyle, plus the discomfort and difficult ramifications of treatment.

> *"I had
> no idea
> that the tears
> of my friends
> would be
> so meaningful."*
>
> *June*

Their tears assured me of their compassion and grounded me in reality. I was persuaded that each one of them would have taken on the cancer for me had it been possible. Now I understand the deeper ministry of *"weep with those who weep"* [ROMANS 12:15 NKJV].

Gather a Group to Pray

3

Barbara immediately called a group of my friends and then let me know that the next evening they would be coming to my home to have a time of prayer with me. I was really surprised at their immediate response. Then later, prior to each of the two surgeries, they encircled me, each petitioning God on my behalf. Henry led us beautifully.

I shouldn't have been surprised by their prayerful hearts because the Bible says, *"In everything, by prayer and petition, with thanksgiving, present your requests to God. And the peace of God, which transcends all understanding, will guard your hearts and your minds in Christ Jesus"* [PHILIPPIANS 4:6–7].

These times of prayer truly provided a precious peace that guarded my heart and guarded my mind.

"The prayer of a righteous man is powerful and effective." [JAMES 5:16]

> *"In everything, by prayer and petition, with thanksgiving, present your requests to God. And the peace of God, which transcends all understanding, will guard your hearts and your minds in Christ Jesus."*
>
> *Philippians 4:6-7*

4 Focus on Family Involvement

The day after my diagnosis, Kay called my brother, Ray — a very active businessman — to see if he and his wife, Nancy Ann, could come to my home at 6:30. (I knew my friends were coming an hour later.) I had something I needed to talk with them about face-to-face. This was the first time I had made such a request.

They arrived at 6:30 sharp. Not only did they respond with great encouragement and listen attentively and compassionately, but Ray also offered help that only he could give. Over the next few days, he talked with several trusted friends who were medical experts and heads of medical institutions. The result of his networking gave me confidence that I was consulting the right doctors to learn about my different treatment options.

But most special to me was the night after surgery, when he came by himself to the hospital and held my hand, simply comforting me with his presence. During this time of uncertainty, Ray really represented the verse that says, *"A brother is born for adversity"* [PROVERBS 17:17].

Give Time-tested Advice

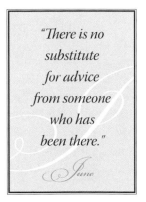

5

There is no substitute for advice from someone who has been there. Sue, my "voice of experience" friend, gave me practical, sound advice. Some advice I really didn't want to hear . . . advice like, *"There will be times when your body will simply stop. June, you can't just push through like you've been accustomed to doing. You'll have to allow yourself to lie down and rest."*

In a matter of weeks, I received a wealth of helpful, time-tested advice from around the country . . . from others who had "been there."

> *"There is no substitute for advice from someone who has been there."*
>
> *June*

In truth, I didn't really believe that Sue's advice would apply to me . . . until after my first chemo treatment when my body seemed to stop. *"My get up and go had got up and went!"* (Perhaps that's why the twenty-third Psalm says, *"He makes me lie down in green pastures."*) Obviously this is a time when the physical body needs more rest than usual.

"Listen now to me and I will give you some advice, and may God be with you." [EXODUS 18:19]

6

Offer Hands-on Help

The next day Sue's daughter, who is a nurse, walked into my bedroom with tears flowing down her cheeks. Suzanne understood. . . . She had been walking down this difficult road with her mother. She assured me that after surgery she would change my dressing and "strip the tubes" so I wouldn't have to make extra trips to the doctor.

Immediately I thought, *Tubes? What tubes? I'll have tubes?*

Obviously, stripping the tubes was a need I had not been told about. Although I learned to drain the tubes myself, just knowing I could call on Suzanne for hands-on help was a genuine comfort.

It's interesting how the Lord brought just the right people my way who had just the right abilities that I needed at the time . . . like John, who carried items I couldn't lift, and Eula, who washed my hair when I couldn't raise my arms. In a very real way, they followed the example of *"the disciples, each according to his ability, decided to provide help"* [ACTS 11:29].

> *"It's interesting how the Lord brought just the right people my way who had just the right abilities."*
>
> *June*

Pen a Meaningful Poem

7

Within two days of the news, I had to leave for Baltimore and New York City to speak at two out-of-town engagements. When I arrived at my hotel in Baltimore, there were flowers awaiting me from "The Mice." (Believe it or not—we are *The Mouseketeers.* We're a group of six friends who, for over 20 years, meet together about four times a year just to support one another.) Attached was a poem penned by Randy.

> To navigate some tough terrain,
> You need some friends, come shine or rain.
> You need a God to see you through,
> The Comforter who makes things new.
> You need a model of peace and duty—
> The memory of your Mother's beauty.
> You need a family that knows what it takes
> To go through trials for each others' sakes.
> You've got the best in order to ace
> This walk of faith with dignity and grace.
> Love, The Mice [1]

After reading these words of encouragement, I immediately tucked the poem into my Bible, where it has stayed ever since. This poem was a tender connection to friends back home, reminding me of their love and support. How true, especially in times of trial, that *"pleasant words are a honeycomb, sweet to the soul and healing to the bones"* [PROVERBS 16:24].

8

Plan to Be Present

When I arrived in New York City, Kimberly, my twenty-seven-year-old niece, called from Seattle, saying, *"I'm coming to Dallas!"* I told her I didn't even know when surgery would be. It didn't matter. . . . She had ordered her nonrefundable ticket.

"I don't know anything about cancer," she said, *"but I want to do research, and I want us to learn as much as we can."*

In reality, the ten days Kim spent in Dallas proved to be a help and comfort beyond compare. She drove me to see my doctor, fetched food for me, and encouraged me to exercise by getting down on the floor with me! (Truthfully, I wouldn't have done those stretching exercises without her!) I think an adaptation of 2 CORINTHIANS 7:6 says it best . . . *"God, who comforts the downcast, comforted [me] by the coming of [Kimberly]."*

At another time, my sister Swanee came in from Boston to help me in a major way, and then later my sister Helen flew in from New Jersey to offer her assistance.

". . . I tell you the truth, whatever you did for one of the least of these brothers of mine, you did for me." [MATTHEW 26:40]

Give the Gift of Song

9

After I returned to Dallas, I was scheduled to have a CAT scan to determine if there were any other abnormalities. Eleanor insisted not only on taking me, but also on being in the procedure room with me. While lying on the table, completely still for 20 minutes, ever so quietly — like a gentle rain — I began to hear her soft voice singing, "No One Ever Cared for Me Like Jesus."

My heart was deeply touched. So unexpected and so sweet were her spiritual songs that seldom-shed tears flowed down my cheeks.

Music can touch the soul like nothing else. I believe that's why the Bible says, *"Speak to one another with psalms, hymns and spiritual songs. Sing and make music in your heart to the Lord"* [EPHESIANS 5:19]. That day, Eleanor's gift of singing touched my heart as nothing else could.

"Sing and make music in your heart to the Lord."

Ephesians 5:19

A few days later I was so surprised to see Rita walk in to deliver the fruit of her own research on cancer, done on my behalf. After sharing her insights, Rita picked up my guitar and sang to me from her heart, playing the most gorgeous music. Rita's rich chords and artistry have always melted my heart. That remarkable evening, Rita blessed my mind and blessed my soul. What an unexpected delight.

10   Keep a Record of Remembrances

At the hospital, my friend Eleanor had the wonderful idea of writing down all the encouraging and helpful kindnesses people extended toward me. She bought an attractive, spiral, hardback book with blank, lined pages that she divided into five sections. Using multicolored tabs, she labeled each section: calls, cards, flowers, food, gifts, visits. Then she recorded within the appropriate section the name of each person who reached out to me and added a brief description of what was said or done.

When I came home from the hospital, she left the book at my home so that others could continue recording each thoughtful deed.

Kimberly also started a book of pictures, along with her fun, handwritten descriptions of events related to my cancer. She always seemed to have a camera in hand — even at the hospital — to capture meaningful images of loved ones visiting or attending to my needs.

Later, as I looked back on the entries in these books, I was able to write appropriate thank-you notes, but even more, the books help me remember each thoughtful deed today. What a treasure those books are to me! I can honestly say . . .

"I thank my God every time I remember you."
[PHILIPPIANS 1:3]

Offer to Communicate Progress and Needs

11

Many people really do care. . . . They really do want to pray. . . . They really do want updates! The problem I seemed to have was the awkwardness of repeatedly talking about myself . . . volunteering information when I was not directly asked.

What a relief when my friend and right-arm assistant, Kay, assumed that role so thoroughly without even being asked.

As Kay gave periodic updates through "June's Journey," she kept my family and friends informed as to my progress throughout my surgery and subsequent chemotherapy and radiation treatments. It was impossible for me to keep everyone posted, and candidly, it was difficult for me to give an objective evaluation of my physical needs and legitimate concerns.

Certain people specifically asked to be included on the relatively small list. How blessed I was to have Kay take the lead and send regular e-mails stating my physical status and mentioning specific prayer requests as well as practical needs. The Bible says,

"We have different gifts . . . . If it is serving, let him serve . . . if it is encouraging, let him encourage; if it is contributing to the needs of others, let him give generously . . . if it is showing mercy, let him do it cheerfully." [ROMANS 12:6 – 8]

At times I began to feel that Kay had all the gifts covered herself!

12 Attend Doctor Appointments

Four friends accompanied me to multiple doctors' appointments in search of the best oncologist for me (an oncologist is a tumor specialist). They wanted not only to lend support but also to hear for themselves in order to fully understand both my illness and my treatment options. Their presence told me, *"We're in this with you, no matter what!"* They took notes, asked questions, processed information, and prayed fervently. (They were careful not to try to make decisions for me.)

"Their presence told me, 'We're in this with you, no matter what!'"

June

While sharing their own perspectives, these friends stood back and allowed God to speak to me about what I should do. I was in the process of making life-altering decisions with long-term ramifications; therefore, I felt I needed guidance to make wise decisions. My "four musketeers" applied the Biblical imperative, *"Let the wise listen and add to their learning, and let the discerning get guidance"* [PROVERBS 1:5].

After interviewing four highly-qualified oncologists, we all felt unanimously guided by the Lord as to which one was right for me. The five of us were in total agreement as to what God had affirmed privately in our individual hearts. What assurance that God had spoken and we all had heard Him!

HOW? WHEN? WHERE? WHY? WHAT?

Bring a Teddy Bear

13

The evening before surgery my doorbell rang. On my front porch was a sight I'll never forget. Five huge overstuffed bears on the shoulders of Bruce and Renee's three daughters and their two young friends ... just to make sure I got *a big bear hug! (Brad was the ring leader of this surprise attack.)*

After seeing my sense of awe, the girls brought the bears inside my home and strategically placed the pack of bears in chairs around my dining room table. Then they placed different items in front of each bear—newspaper, Bible, concordance, and such. What a sight! (Today my studious bears have a place of prominence sitting around my dining table.)

Have you ever thought, *Why are teddy bears so universally considered comforting?* I think it's because their arms are always so wide open, a position that makes us feel loved and accepted. Perhaps that was why it felt so special to receive baby bears from Janice in Las Vegas, Jim in Denver, JoAnn in Dallas, and a purple cub from Phil and Karol all the way from Kentucky.

I am well aware that PSALM 37:21 says, *"The righteous give generously,"* but I had no idea this would include such a generous supply of teddy bears!

14 Lift the Spirit with Laughter

As I was headed into surgery, friends came to the hospital with a unique sense of humor. Cheryl presented me with a pink bedpan with a potted plant placed inside. My "potty plant" evoked instant laughter from the throng of those in the waiting room! Meanwhile, Karen sent "dancing flowers" that twirled to the tune of "Cotton-Eyed Joe."

Imagine a room full of surgery patients, literally laughing out loud, seeing these flowers twirling to "The Cotton-Eyed Joe"!

Over time, I received a bundle of humorous cards — funny cards in which I was being compared to a long-haired dog having a "bad hair day." I smiled at the note to me that said, *"Don't worry about having a bad hair day — soon you won't have any hair!"*

Because these cards were such fun to receive, they "inspired" me to write my own verses to send to others.

If you are in pain
Over losing your mane,
Just think of the lion:
"Bad hair days" leave him sigh'n.
When you feel real sore
'Cause your hair is no more,
Better to have a bald head
Than a head full of lead.

It's interesting how surgery that seems so serious can evoke both tears and laughter . . . and we all need laughter. As the Bible says, there is *"a time to weep and a time to laugh"* [ECCLESIASTES 3:4].

Pin Up Humorous Posters

15

Diane made two hilarious posters—one for each surgery. Imagine a poster with four different candy bars glued to it: Crunch®, Snickers®, Butterfinger®, Air Heads®.[2] In her message to me, she had glued each candy bar in place of the actual word used to spell out the message: *"In a Crunch? No Snickers please. Call Dr. Butterfinger, M.D. at the Air Heads Clinic: call 1-800-BAD-GOOF!"*

Her second poster—blue in color—had 40 white cotton balls in the shape of a big, broad smile. Above the cotton ball smile is this clever sentiment: *"What the doctors have forgotten, you can fill with cotton!"*

No doubt, Diane knew the reality of PROVERBS 15:13, *"A happy heart makes the face cheerful,"* and her posters brought a lot of smiles and a lot of cheer.

16   Say You Can Stay at the Hospital

Be available to stay in the hospital overnight. A team of friends made arrangements as to who would stay with me at the hospital. Diane and June took the first surgery; Eleanor and Cheryl took the second. They fed me ice chips, put petroleum jelly on my lips, and helped me get in and out of bed. Their offer proved to be absolutely essential because, to my surprise, I had no physical stability.

Never have I fully appreciated the literal meaning of ECCLESIASTES 4:9–10, *"Two are better than one . . . if one falls down, his friend can help him up. But pity the man who falls and has no one to help him up!"* The truth is, if my friends had not been there for me, I literally would have fallen! I needed to lean on my friends.

Look for Little Tokens of Love

17

Eleanor gave me my first token of love—a blue and white porcelain cross with these words: *"Is anything too hard for God?"* [GENESIS 18:14]. Cheryl handed me a Noah's ark magnet to remind me that God will keep His covenant with me ... and from Karen, a crocheted angel—a reminder that my guardian angel is watching over me.

Marcia gave me a little, green, velvet pillow with embroidered roses that simply says, "Hugs." I love this petite pillow with its one word message. Hugs promote emotional healing and can be freely given and received by one and all. How true that ...

"A word aptly spoken is like apples of gold in settings of silver." [PROVERBS 25:11]

How creative! A hand-decorated water bottle that soothed more than my aches ... it warmed my heart.

Cancer can be a "bitter pill," but this larger-than-life capsule (filled with 100 real pills) was a fun way to take pain relievers ... made me feel like a little kid again!

18 Make the First Move and Speak Wisely

I remember missing Maureen at our HOPE FOR THE HEART staff retreat the day after I returned from New York City (a week after confirmation of my diagnosis). I wondered why she wasn't there since she had always faithfully attended in the past. I later learned that she felt too awkward because she didn't know what to say. While she felt guilty for staying away, she also felt uneasy coming close. So I made the first move toward her.

Pam also avoided me, not because she was at a loss for words, but because my illness reminded her of her mother's recent death from cancer. Seeing me became a trigger of painful memories rising in her heart and mind, so she sought personal protection by keeping her distance. Again, I made the first (and second) move toward her and I know she was glad.

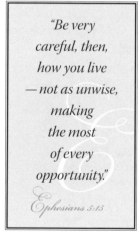

"Be very careful, then, how you live — not as unwise, making the most of every opportunity."

Ephesians 5:15

Therefore, don't avoid those with cancer. (And tell your loved ones, "Don't take it personally if someone fails to respond, viewing it as rejection of you, but rather view it as reaction to cancer. Some people worry that they might upset you by saying the wrong thing. You can help them by talking openly with them. This can help alleviate their worry and fear.")

"Be very careful, then, how you live — not as unwise, making the most of every opportunity." [EPHESIANS 5:15]

Don't fail to call.

When you first hear the news that someone has cancer, even if you feel at a loss for words, don't hesitate to call to say, "I'm so sorry. . . . I care. . . . I'm here for you. . . . I'm praying for God's wisdom, healing, and peace for you."

Don't withdraw.

Some people withdraw from their loved ones who have cancer because they don't know what to say, or because it stirs up painful memories, or because it's too painful to face.

Instead, simply say, "I'm so sorry; I really don't know what to say." These words are sufficient—the conversation will naturally proceed from there. Meanwhile, you've let your loved one know you care.

Don't relate horror stories.

If someone you know has cancer, don't tell bad experiences about a hospital stay or negative stories about a treatment. Instead of speaking words of horror, speak words of hope, "I know God will give you strength for whatever you need to endure. . . . I'm praying for God's peace to be present within you, every single day."

19 Offer to Be a "Go-fer"

Sometimes the offer to run an errand was a lifesaver—especially when it had to do with picking up pain medication on my way home from the hospital right after surgery or prescriptions to fight nausea. (Thank you, Barbara!)

Little did I know that, because of having chemo, queasiness would be a constant companion. Nor did I know that the salt in chicken soup would quell the queasiness. That's why, when I needed to be present for our ministry's International Task Force meetings, Mickey's offer to "go-fer" anything was such a big help. In a jiffy, he brought me eight cans of beef boullion and chicken broth!

And never will I forget the Saturday afternoon when Gail emphatically informed me, *"For mouth sores, take four tablets of acidophilus with goat's milk several times a day."* Before I knew it, Kay was out the door and back. Did the capsules work? You bet they did. . . . they helped within eight hours! But most memorable to me was that I didn't ever have to ask Kay for help. . . She simply saw a need and met it. How true that *"a friend loves at all times"* [PROVERBS 17:17] and offers to "go-fer" anything!

Prepare a Rotation Plan for Primary Home Care

20

Friends banded together to anticipate my future needs and to coordinate a schedule so that I wouldn't even have to THINK about the details. (For several weeks, three friends—Eleanor, June, and Barbara—rotated each night, sleeping on a flip bed in my bedroom.) They set in motion a plan for accomplishing each task so that I did not even have to *ask* for help.

It was beautiful to see them working together to provide for my needs . . . not with the intent of doing what they would most enjoy doing, but rather doing what I really needed. Even though I knew the situation was burdensome, they didn't make me feel that I was a burden. With sweet attentiveness and joyful spirits they carried out Paul's directive,

"Carry each other's burdens, and in this way you will fulfill the law of Christ."
[GALATIANS 6:2]

"It was beautiful to see them working together to provide for my needs."

June

"Carry each other's burdens, and in this way you will fulfill the law of Christ."

Galatians 6:2

21 ## Bring Helpful Books, Videos, and Booklets

Val and Susan sent three books on cancer that they knew would be helpful . . . and Suzanne gave me two. Nancy sent me a video. People from all over the country—people whom I didn't know personally—were amazingly caring in that regard. They and other friends gave me pamphlets, articles, and advice about people who had already walked this challenging path.

I was eager to receive authoritative information, for the more I learned, the more confident I felt. I was eager to *"listen to advice and accept instruction"* because I knew Proverbs 19:20 said, *"in the end you will be wise."*

> *"Friends gave me pamphlets, articles, and advice about people who had already walked this challenging path."*
>
> *June*

Initially, I knew very little about cancer. Although my father had died of colon cancer and my mother of liver cancer, I barely knew the basics, and I needed to know more. For example:

- **"What is cancer?"** Cancer or *carcinoma* is a malignant, uncontrolled growth of cells.[3]

- **"When does cancer begin?"** Cancer begins when a normal cell changes into a cell with an abnormal growth pattern—a cell that abnormally divides and grows.

- **"How fast does breast cancer grow?"** An average tumor doubles every 100 days. When it reaches one centimeter (3/8 inch)—the size of the tip of your smallest finger—it has been in your body approximately eight to ten years. This tumor has grown from one cell to approximately 100 billion cells.[4]

- **"How does cancer spread (or metastasize)?"** When cancer cells break away from their original location, they can travel through the blood vessels or lymph system to other sites and form secondary tumors. This spreading to a distant site is called metastasis.

  And this has been my number one objective regarding cancer: to do all that I can to keep it from metastasizing.

22 Ask Appropriate Questions

From the moment I received my diagnosis, and throughout the next nine months, I felt as if I had been swept away by a mammoth tidal wave and swiftly carried off to some unfamiliar country where everyone spoke a strange language ... at least a language totally foreign to my ears. Clearly, I did not know the language or lingo of cancer.

Consequently, my crash course in "Cancer 101" proved to be invaluable—but only so because of my loved ones who also entered into the schooling by listening and asking appropriate questions. Getting as much information as possible concerning my particular types of cancer (I had two types) was essential. Educating ourselves is particularly helpful because knowledge instills confidence and a degree of control over our lives. Knowledge also decreases fear and anxiety. Therefore, following surgery and prior to the meeting with my oncologist, we tried to compile a list of questions, such as:

- **"What is the size of the tumor(s)?"** I had two tumors, both classified as "T2."

Tumor Classifications[5] *(measured in centimeters)*	
T0	No tumor is reported and there are no signs of spread to lymph nodes or tissues beyond the breast.
T1	2 centimeters (cm) or smaller
T2	2–5 cm
T3	5+ cm
T4	Any size tumor that has spread to the chest wall or skin

- **"What is the stage of the cancer?"** Breast cancer is identified by stages. Mine was Stage II because it was under 5 cm, it wasn't in the lymph nodes, and it had not metastasized.

Cancer Stages[6]	
Stage I	T1-T2 cm or smaller with no lymph nodes involved
Stage II	T0-T2 with one lymph node involved T2-T3 with zero lymph nodes involved
Stage III	T0-T3 with 2+ lymph nodes involved T3 or 4 with one lymph node involved
Stage IV	Any size tumor metastasized (spread to distant location)

- **"Does the cancer have other important tumor characteristics?"** I had some cancer cells in my lymph glands.

- "**What are the options for treatment?"** Surgery, chemotherapy, radiation, hormone blockers—I had it all!

- **"What are the percentages of benefit (cure rates) for each option?"**

- **"What are the risks of each option? What are the possible temporary and long-term side effects?"**

- **"What are the possible side effects and how should they be treated?"**

  See list of "Tips" in this book.

- **"Is the cancer estrogen-receptor positive?"**
  Mine was. Therefore, I was told that taking a hormone
  blocker could be highly effective to avoid the
  recurrence of cancer.

- **"Is the tumor slow growing or fast growing?"** I had
  one of each on each side—lucky me!

- **"What is the likelihood of recurrence after
  treatment? What year markers are significant
  to pass?"** For example, once I passed 3 1/2 years with no
  recurrence of cancer, I rejoiced because fast-growing cancer
  typically recurs within the first two to three years.

- **"Is this type of cancer genetic?"** BRAC1 and/or
  BRAC2 Genetic Testing can determine if there is a
  susceptibility to hereditary cancer genes. Ninety-five percent
  of breast cancer is not hereditary, and my cancer was not.[7]

- **"Are there known causes for this kind of cancer?"**
  Mine was unknown.

- **"What helpful books, materials, or support groups
  would you recommend?"** Realize that no question is
  "stupid" or unimportant—especially when it concerns
  the physical, mental, or emotional health of anyone going
  through cancer treatment. We all need to ask as many
  questions as necessary in order to make informed decisions
  and to feel a sense of responsibility for our treatment. That
  is why the Bible says,

  *"The heart of the discerning acquires knowledge; the ears of
  the wise seek it out."* [PROVERBS 18:15]

Invest Energy in the Internet

23

You can search the Internet for extensive information on any illness—on any cancer.

Imagine my surprise when one evening Rita walked into my home with reams of paper—three days worth of research on cancer! I could hardly believe the time and energy she invested. She lived out PROVERBS 15:14, *"The discerning heart seeks knowledge."*

One fact is clear—after you read page after page after page on the Internet, you are able to distill the major points into simple, understandable terms. For example, it really helps to understand how different treatments for cancer work.

How Does Chemotherapy Work?[8]

- Chemotherapy is the use of toxic drugs in an attempt to destroy cancer cells. While surgery and radiation remove and destroy cancer cells in a specific area, chemotherapy works to kill cancer throughout the entire body.

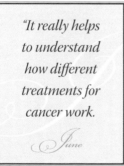

"It really helps to understand how different treatments for cancer work.

June

- Chemo also affects normal, healthy cells, causing side effects that typically impact the blood, hair, mouth, digestive tract, and reproductive system. Some people feel minimal impact, while others experience greater effects.

- More than 100 chemotherapy drugs are used in various combinations ("combination chemotherapy"). Each drug performs a different function and works together to kill more cancer cells.

How Does Radiation Work?[9]

- Radiation therapy beams specific doses of high energy waves (x-rays) at tumors or areas of the body where tumors have been removed or where there is disease.

- These high doses of radiation kill cells or keep them from growing and reproducing (dividing into two cells).

How Does Hormone Therapy Work?[10]

- Some cancer growths are fed by the hormones estrogen and progesterone.

- Oral drugs called "hormone blockers" are needed to either lower or block the hormone levels in order to prevent the recurrence of cancer.

Exert Initiative to Exercise

24

A few days following each surgery, I needed to begin a regime of regular exercise—I needed to stretch muscles that were naturally drawing up during the healing process. But exercise was an unwanted companion because it was too uncomfortable.

To encourage me to do what I didn't want to do, Kim came in with a cheery voice, *"Let's do some exercise!"* Well, I didn't want to disappoint my niece and seem like a "fuddy-duddy," so I would do whatever she wanted me to do. What a help!

Starting a new habit is not easy and requires setting aside needed time in your daily schedule. It takes dedication to the cause and determination to reach the goal.

Encourage your loved one who is facing this physical and mental challenge, offer to "make it a twosome" for the first week or so, and lead the two of you in the required exercises. Just having someone there to share the experience, to acknowledge the difficulty, and to cheer the accomplishments will give incentive and prevent procrastination.

If your loved one feels physically discouraged, you might share these words of wisdom . . .

"I can do everything through him who gives me strength."
[PHILIPPIANS 4:13]

25

Buy New Sleepwear

Surgery makes mobility difficult at best. That's why the two identical gifts — intentionally identical gowns — one from Lillian, the other from her daughter, Barbara, were such a relief. They knew I would adore the soft, new blue plaid gowns.

The fact that they buttoned down the front made them easier and less painful to get on and off (my arms didn't want to cooperate!). Barbara and Lillian knew the gown ordeal would be a challenge after surgery. Adding to their thoughtfulness, they also gave me a blue plaid robe to match!

"The Bible says, "God loves a cheerful giver."

2 Corinthians 9:7

God sure must love my friends!

My friend June also gave me a soft, blue cotton gown for the hotter months — again, one that buttoned down the front. (I had no idea that my skin would be so sensitive following surgery.)

The Bible says, *"God loves a cheerful giver."* [2 CORINTHIANS 9:7]

God sure must love my friends!

Offer Help for the Holidays

26

Before my second surgery, my Boston sister, Swanee, announced that she was flying to Dallas to take care of me throughout the Thanksgiving holidays. *"Your friends can all be with their families, and that will give them some needed time off."* Instead of traditionally being with her husband's family, Swanee flew in Wednesday evening and stayed until Sunday evening.

Since my mobility was sorely lacking following two surgeries, she was extremely helpful—beyond description. She even bought me a leather, rocker recliner, which made getting up much easier with an "alley oop." Without trying to be Scriptural, Swanee exemplified JOSHUA 1:14–15,

"You are to help your brothers [and sister!] until the LORD gives them rest."

Oh, did she help!

27 Fix Enough Food ... for Caregivers Too

No "sick bay" list could be complete without the mention of "meals on wheels." From Linda to Lillian ... Kathy to Kelli ... Muriel to Maggie ... Jane, Jack and Janie, every morsel brought over by friends satisfied palates and helped to lighten the load of my caregivers.

On Thanksgiving Day, Kelli took to heart NEHEMIAH 8:10, *"Go and enjoy choice food and sweet drinks, and send some to those who have nothing prepared."* She sent over a scrumptious, multicourse dinner for my sister and me. Lillian provided our dining entertainment by quoting a precious Christmas poem she had memorized as a child.

> *"Every morsel brought over by friends satisfied palates and helped to lighten the load of my caregivers."*
>
> *June*

One day my nephew Hunter and his new wife, Stephanie, came to see me. I was still bedridden. They made me feel like a queen holding court — bedside. They brought some delectable food, but most of all, I valued their making time to visit. Then, a few weeks later, Ashlee, Hunter's sister, dropped by with a mouthwatering Italian dish that was immensely appreciated by everyone. Within the month, my niece was back again with her "meals on wheels."

Those who came with food were extra caring — bringing food in disposable containers that didn't need to be returned. That's extra thoughtful!

Bring a Bouquet, Plant, or Helium Balloon

28

There's a reason why flowers are typically sent during times of sadness or sickness. Flowers bring beauty to people in pain — floral bouquets bring "sunshine" to any setting.

On the other hand, a plant can last for months and sometimes for years. For example, following my first surgery, Bob and Ruth brought to my bedside a small but sturdy green plant in a classic, blue and white, porcelain container . . . and it's still hearty and thriving.

And of course, the huge helium balloon with bright ribbons and bows and a big smiley face was a tremendous hit. Such a gift would brighten any corner!

Of course, the clever "cookie bouquet" was irresistible — especially to those with a sweet tooth.

The good news is: Whether it's a bouquet from Gil and Ann, a plant, or a balloon from Ray and Nancy Ann, they each say, *"We care. . . . You matter. . . . You are loved."*

"Like cold water to a weary soul is good news from a distant land." [PROVERBS 25:25]

Seek Ways to Assuage Anxiety

29

The day of my first chemotherapy treatment, Barbara arrived early at my home simply to pray with me. What a time for prayer—I needed peace.

Then, after my friend June drove me to the hospital, she sought to calm my apprehension by reading the December 7 selections from both of the classic daily devotionals, *Streams in the Desert* and *My Utmost for His Highest.*

I'll have to admit that I had difficulty concentrating because of all the "horror stories" I had heard about chemotherapy. But I so appreciated her efforts and valued her concern. And reading to me did calm some of my anxiety.

"Encourage one another and build each other up."
1 Thessalonians 5:11

Then, "out of the blue," as I was walking into the treatment center, my sister Swanee called from Boston just to give me a boost. What a surprise. Her call was the encouragement that I sorely needed.

Apparently, they all had discerned that I might feel anxious prior to my first chemo series ... and they were right. They gave me just what I needed that unforgettable day. They did what the Scripture says to do ...

"Encourage one another and build each other up."
[1 THESSALONIANS 5:11]

Help to Hunt for Head Covers

30

I knew I would lose my hair between days 14 and 17 following my first chemo treatment. My head would soon be bald, a result of aggressive chemotherapy; therefore, I knew I needed to buy a wig. One problem: wig shopping was totally unfamiliar territory!

Fortunately, Nancy Ann researched the most popular wig shops in Dallas. Meanwhile, Maggie suggested Mimi's, which was at the top of Nancy Ann's list. On day 14, my friend June took me on the journey to select my "new do" (as in hair do).

When we arrived at Mimi's, I remember sitting in the car with tears in my eyes thinking, I can't believe this is happening —this is so surreal. Yet my cancer was *very real,* and I chose to face that fact with faith, not fear.

After going inside and trying on one particular wig, I began to think, I like this wig better than my own hair—this isn't so bad after all!

Maggie, who is known for her humor, said, "If someone asks, 'Is that your hair?' say, 'It sure is! I paid a pretty penny for it!'"

And sweet-spirited Nicole sent me a "care package" of wonderful, stretch head coverings in a variety of colors. They were for my bald head so that I would not catch "my

How many symphony conductors would don a "Goofy" hat just to make you grin? After losing my hair, my brother-in-law Charles wore this hat the entire evening —now, that's really goofy!

death of cold" (as my grandmother used to say). Everyone did their very best to help as an expression of the love of God. *"Because you are my help, I sing in the shadow of your wings."* [PSALM 63:7]

31 Encourage a "Journal for the Journey"

Journaling can take many forms. Some people feel emotionally stuck in their pain. Journaling can help them get unstuck!

When people process their experiences on paper, the

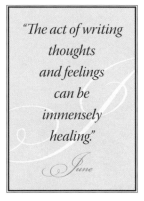

"The act of writing thoughts and feelings can be immensely healing."

June

act of writing their thoughts and feelings — expressing their anxieties and fears — can be immensely healing. Some emotions are difficult to express. Keeping a journal of the daily struggles and victories along with the thoughts that accompany them can be a cathartic exercise.

Encourage your loved one to consider journaling in order to help draw out difficult emotions that need to be surfaced. Later, they can look back at their journal and help someone else on the same journey.

"The purposes of a man's heart are deep waters, but a man of understanding draws them out." [PROVERBS 20:5]

What you are reading right now is a type of journal about my own journey through cancer. Writing down all the different ways that people reached out and blessed me has, in turn, enabled me to reach out and bless others.

Make a Chart for Medications

32

Connie contributed a valuable treasure. She constructed a chart of the various medications I was to take. It contained the name of each pill, each injection, and each fluid with a description of its purpose and the time each was to be taken throughout my treatment regime. This wonderfully detailed chart grew over time and proved to be invaluable both to me and to my caregivers.

With pills and shots being added along the way, by the time I'd had my fourth chemotherapy treatment, I couldn't go even a few hours without taking a pill, giving myself an injection, eating a particular food, or drinking a particular drink. Keeping the schedule straight seemed next to impossible.

Connie's chart saved me from feeling that I was drowning in a sea of medications. I needed help in holding on to my doctor's instructions in order to do what was truly best for my physical body! *"Hold on to instruction, do not let it go; guard it well, for it is your life"* [PROVERBS 4:13].

Medicine Chart

Medicine	Purpose	Dosage	Time
A	Nausea	1 Pill	8, 12, 4
B	Blood Count	10 mg Shot	8, 12, 4
C	Pain	1 Patch	Every 48 hrs
D	Fatigue	8 oz	10, 6

33 Remind Gently of the Routine

"Have you taken all your pills yet?" . . .

"Do you need your anti-nausea meds?" . . .

"What about your antibiotics?" . . .

Is asking such questions necessary? Normally, I wouldn't think so; however, after my fourth cycle of chemotherapy, I think I slipped into "chemo brain."

Yes, you heard correctly: CHEMO BRAIN! (When I first read about chemo brain, I laughed out loud!) Apparently, after a certain number of treatments, the memory can be temporarily affected.

I've even read that chemo brain (or chemofog) can last up to ten years! As a result, I've told everyone I know that I'm going to take full advantage of this label for as long as I can. Anytime I forget anything, I get to claim "chemo brain!" In fact, I told all my friends that I would share the label with them so that when they are forgetful, they too can claim chemo brain by osmosis! (They love it.)

In truth, gentle reminders were "welcomed friends" to me . . . friends because of the times I tended to forget something important. I am grateful to my faithful family of friends who have enabled me to be wiser because of their helpful hints. They were most aware that *"wisdom preserves the life of its possessor"* [ECCLESIASTES 7:12].

Find Items Frequently Forgotten

34

Karen, whom I've never met, sent a small basket, the perfect size to hold my pill bottles. This was a basket she had ordered for herself, but instead sent it to me. How helpful ... and how selfless! Don, a longtime friend, brought his favorite CD of songs that he has loved for years. Pat knew of my tendency to be very cold-natured and brought soft, warm blankets to ward off the cold.

And my dear friend Dorothy—the queen of hospitality and practicality—didn't limit her generosity to just one item, but instead sent an assortment of little treasures:

- thank-you cards and stamps

- a bag of hard candy "for the nurses"

- a pocket-sized case with three pill bottles

- two crossword puzzle books with pencils

- a card of encouragement containing a message from the heart of God ...

"When you pass through the waters, I will be with you; and when you pass through the rivers, they will not sweep over you. When you walk through the fire, you will not be burned; the flames will not set you ablaze." [ISAIAH 43:2]

Thanks to Dorothy, I could express gratitude to others through the cards she so thoughtfully sent to me.

35 Put Together a Scrapbook of Pictures

Every few days I seemed to receive a surprise treat from Helen, my New York/New Jersey sister. Initially Helen asked me if there was anything that I would like. I answered, "Yes, I would love some family pictures."

In a matter of days, the first scrapbook arrived. It was full of fun, family pictures that brought back many memories. Obviously, Helen went through bundles of snapshots, cut out the important part of the select pictures, and then contoured each photograph, which gave them a special animated look. The second scrapbook was definitely an endearing labor of love. This scrapbook is one that I will treasure for a lifetime!

And so special is Helen's hand-drawn Scripture, that it is now displayed on my bedroom wall: *"For God hath not given us the spirit of fear; but of power, and of love, and of a sound mind"* [2 TIMOTHY 1:7 KJV].

There is nothing like seeing truth every day to keep me free from fear.

Fix Food That Helps with Healing

36

Can you imagine not having any desire to eat steak! Well, because of chemotherapy, I experienced some surprising changes. I lost my desire for sweets (that was actually good), and I lost my desire for meats (that was actually not so good).

Because I had such difficulty chewing meat (because of mouth sores), and because I continually struggled with a low red blood cell count (I was anemic), Jack came to my home, donned his chef's hat, and prepared a steak. More accurately, he simmered a number of steaks for me to drink! Jack knew I needed the beneficial nutrients in red meat.

Chef Jack's Beef Broth

> 2 lbs. round roast or steak
>
> 1 Crock-Pot
>
> **Cut meat** into small pieces and put into the Crock-Pot.
>
> **Cook on Low overnight.**
>
> **Pour** broth into a pint jar, and put meat in a strainer and squeeze. Press with a spoon until all the broth is removed.
>
> **Refrigerate.** When chilled, remove fat with a spoon. When ready to serve, pour into a cup, heat, and serve.

(Note: If your loved one's liver has difficulty processing iron, check with your doctor before preparing this high protein broth.)

Bon appétit from Chef Jack. *Bon appétit!*[11]

"[The Lord] satisfies your desires with good things so that your youth is renewed like the eagle's." [PSALM 103:5]

37

Help Your Loved One Live with Lymphedema

In February I flew to Nashville to speak at a large convention. That evening I was shocked to see that my right hand and arm were red and swollen—they seemed huge! Immediately, I called my oncologist, who told me to come see her as soon as I returned. She explained that the swelling in my arm was lymphedema: an accumulation of lymph fluid in soft tissues, which causes swelling (edema refers to swelling).

Upon return, I received a lymph massage, a special type of wrapping and a pressure sleeve and gauntlet. Every time I fly in an airplane, I must wear my pressure sleeve to avoid swelling.

Between 20% and 30% of those who have had lymph nodes removed experience lymphedema.[12] A pressure sleeve and a pressure gauntlet can help alleviate swelling. If your loved one is experiencing this sort of swelling, encourage them to seek the doctor's help.

Our blood carries *lymphatic fluid,* which contains many good nutrients, throughout our bodies. Lymph nodes filter out bacteria, toxins, and waste products from the lymphatic fluid. Think of lymphedema as a plumbing problem. Our veins and lymphatic channels are like pipes and drains meant to handle the normal flow of lymphatic fluid. If these lymph nodes and channels are removed, we may not have enough pipes and drains to eliminate all the fluid.

Wearing a pressure sleeve for the arm and a pressure gauntlet for the hand will help alleviate swelling. Meanwhile, remember . . .

"We are hard pressed on every side, but not crushed; perplexed, but not in despair." [2 CORINTHIANS 4:8]

Provide Comfy Clothes   38

Forget about my former pullover sweaters . . . or pullover anything! I had no idea how sensitive my skin would be after surgery. That is why I was so grateful when Nancy Ann brought an assortment of comfy button-up tops (. . . as well as desserts to die for and a stuffed cat stitched with "You're the cat's meow").

Just think, you may be the "angel of mercy" that God will use to provide loose-fitting clothing and shoes for your friend by either loaning them or purchasing them. (Some items "on loan" are appropriate because after chemotherapy much of the fluid retention and weight gain is lost.) Just make sure the clothing doesn't irritate or put pressure on the skin, especially on areas sensitive as a result of cancer treatment.

The issue of clothes began to be a problem as I looked forward to Heather's wedding. Ray and Nancy Ann's daughter was getting married, and because of the steroids in my chemo medication, I had ballooned up an extra 35 pounds and couldn't wear anything I owned that was appropriate for a wedding.

How well I remember the day when Nancy Ann called me at HOPE FOR THE HEART. She knew I was not able to endure the rigors of shopping, so she brought the shop to me! She was on her way with five outfits that she had handpicked for me to try on. One was simply perfect!

Since the Bible says, *"It is more blessed to give than to receive"* [ACTS 20:35], Nancy Ann surely must be blessed!

39 Be Sensitive about Special Occasions

Four weeks before the wedding, I could no longer wear any of the shoes that I owned — my feet were too swollen. One day I was talking with my brother on the telephone and shared my predicament. *"Ray, I've gained so much weight, and there's absolutely nothing I can do to stop it!"*

Never will I forget his words, *"June, it doesn't matter. We just want you there for the wedding. You can come barefoot!"* Wow! He would not be embarrassed — even if I looked like a blimp! (Tears came to my eyes.... He never knew.) He just wanted me there to share in the special occasion.

How good of him to speak such comforting words in the midst of my embarrassment. As PROVERBS 15:23 says, *"A man finds joy in giving an apt reply — and how good is a timely word!"*

As I donned my new size 10 shoes (normally size 9) for the wedding, I gave thanks that I wouldn't have to walk down the aisle barefoot! On the evening of the wedding reception, my sister Swanee was phenomenal. Bless her heart, she knew

I needed help, and without a word from me, she took on the job. And what a help she was! She offered her hand to help me up the stairs. (I could stand without back pain for only a few minutes.)

During the reception she seated me in a chair to ease my pain, and then as she mingled among guests, she proceeded to escort friends and family over to where she had me stationed. Later, when I had to leave early (the one and only time I've ever left early from anything!), Swanee left her family at the hotel, drove me home, put me

"A man finds joy in giving an apt reply."

Proverbs 15:3

to bed, stayed the night, and helped me the next morning to get ready for the "day after" brunch. Truly, her sensitivity was endearing, and her servanthood was extraordinary. Swanee indeed lived out ...

"Serve one another in love." [GALATIANS 5:13]

40

Be Ready to Donate Blood

As the chemo treatments took their toll on my body, they also assaulted my blood. Simply put, my platelets were dangerously low. (Platelets play a crucial part in the blood clotting process by forming a "platelet plug," which stops bleeding and allows injuries to heal.)

Because I had a low platelet count, I bruised easily. I had difficulty stopping nosebleeds, as well as normal bleeding from the needle pricks. Thus, I needed several "platelet transfusions"—ASAP! My friend June drove me to the hospital and immediately donated blood. Within the hour, Cheryl called and volunteered to do the same. However, a chaplain who worked at the hospital had just walked in to donate blood for anyone (me, in this case) who needed it.

Though I never had the opportunity to thank that chaplain, I literally thank God for people like him who are so willing to give of themselves. (In an effort to track down the chaplain, I have since learned that many chaplains and hospital staff members donate their blood on a regular basis.)

Many people are unaware that an excessively low platelet count can cause a person literally to bleed to death internally. This health risk must be taken seriously. In fact, I was not allowed to travel more than 20 minutes from the hospital . . . just in case bleeding started and didn't stop. The Bible has made it clear that *"the life of a creature is in the blood"* [LEVITICUS 17:11]. Therefore, realize that when you volunteer to give your blood, you are actually being a lifesaver!

Convey God's Hope on Heart-shaped Cutouts

41

One of the most creative gifts I received was a red, heart-shaped candy box (minus the candy) filled with many personalized messages. Someone I do not know personally — a dedicated listener to our daily broadcasts from Hope For The Heart — cut out about 20 small, medium, and large paper hearts from pink construction paper. On each heart she wrote a different Scripture that included the word **heart**, and then she personalized each Scripture with my name.

How precious to see PSALM 69:32 KJV written at the top followed by the words: *"The humble shall see this, and be glad: and your **heart** [June] shall live."*

And another, *"Give . . . your servant [June] an understanding **heart** to judge thy people, that [she] may discern between good and bad"* [1 KINGS 3:9 KJV].

And still another, *"I have found [June] . . . a [woman] after my own **heart"*** [ACTS 13:22].

Oh, how these tender messages warmed my heart!

42

Consider a Cancer Support Group

Several years before my illness, two of my neighbors were diagnosed with cancer. One day, Carolyn told me about the cancer support group that was held at her home and what a blessing it was for her, as well as Ruth. They could laugh together, cry together, and be unguarded before each other . . . together.

Among old and new friends they were able to talk about their frustrations and fears and how to face the future . . . about how they could each help their husbands . . . help their children . . . help each other . . . and help even themselves.

Perhaps you could encourage your loved one to join such a group; perhaps help find a group and then go to the first meeting with your friend. Although I wasn't in that group, because of the help from my extraordinary friends, I learned the vital role of heartfelt support, care, and encouragement. I could honestly say to them, *"Your love has given me great joy and encouragement."* [PHILEMON 7]. I couldn't have made it without them.

Plan a Regular Time to Pray

43

Recently, I saw Dave at a large, festive gathering, and we began to talk. At the conclusion of our conversation, his words were a surprise to me ... *"June, I want you to know that a day doesn't go by that I do not pray for you. I pray for you every day."* I was deeply moved and amazed—I had no idea.

Just as discipline is required when establishing a new habit or beginning a new routine, discipline is also needed when planning to pray for your loved one on a regular basis. Look at your schedule and determine the time each day when you can arrange to be alone with God and lift up your loved one to Him. (I know that Esther Beth and Orville, Swann, Mary Nance, and Hannah pray each day for me.)

Give your loved one an opportunity to express needs and concerns so that you can pray knowledgeably. Specifically ask, "What would you like for me to pray about?" or "What is most challenging for you right now?" And if possible, let your loved one know the exact time you will be praying.

"Far be it from me that I should sin against the LORD by failing to pray for you." [1 SAMUEL 12:23]

44   Consider a "Cancer Walk"

My heart was encouraged when I realized that my loved ones were not only concerned about my individual battle with cancer, but also cared about defeating cancer for everyone else. The American Cancer Society sponsors a "Cancer Walk" designed to raise awareness, foster camaraderie, and raise funds for breast cancer research, patient services, education, and advocacy.

Participants can walk in their own cities. My sister Helen walked in my name in her local "Cancer Walk" on the East Coast, and my niece Kim participated in a mini-triathlon on the West Coast. My friend Janie did a walk to raise funds in Dallas, while her husband, Jack, rode a motorcycle to provide safety for the Dallas walkers. How special to know that their efforts could help defeat this common enemy.

My sister Helen walked in New Jersey, not to solicit funds, but to love and support me. She wrote to our family members encouraging them to walk around the block and to think of me during that time. What a marvelous act of love from my family!

A year after my surgery it was my turn. I was blessed to be able to encourage Val by sponsoring her fundraising walk for Susan. I personally believe that a cancer walk offers encouragement to the sponsor and to the walker, as well as to the person battling cancer.

Those who support cancer patients can pray this Scripture for them . . .

"He gives strength to the weary and increases the power of the weak. . . . Those who hope in the Lord will renew their strength. They will soar on wings like eagles; they will run and not grow weary, they will walk and not be faint."
[ISAIAH 40:29–31]

Give an Engraved Bracelet

45

After my diagnosis, my "forever friend" Barbara learned that she had breast cancer. This news hit many of us hard because my joyful, easygoing friend, who is always helping others, is anything but sickly. Barbara is not just a staff counselor, but also an inspiring friend "who walks her talk!"

The team within our Christian counseling ministry wanted to do something extra special for Barbara so we decided to give her a wideband, slip-on, silver bracelet. On the outside is engraved, *"Fear not, for I am with you [Isaiah 41:10]."* Engraved on the inside are the initials of each staff member—all 48 of us!

Today as she wraps the bracelet around her wrist, it serves as a constant reminder of our love for her and our prayers to God on her behalf. The silver band also serves as a comforting assurance from the Lord, who says,

"Do not fear, for I am with you; do not be dismayed, for I am your God. I will strengthen you and help you; I will uphold you with my righteous right hand." [ISAIAH 41:10]

46

Help Out at Home

While some say, "A man's home is his castle," maintaining the castle can be a challenge when someone in the family is in recovery. The extraordinary thoughtfulness of my loved ones was quite evident by their willingness to keep my home in order.

Vacuuming and sweeping, laundry and lifting are easy before surgery . . . but right after surgery, these tasks are impossible. Offering to mow the lawn, empty the trash, and do small repairs are wonderful ways to help.

Not having to worry about housework or yard work is a great gift! Often I found it difficult to ask for personal help, yet I can unequivocally say that these words reflect the compassionate care of my sacrificial helpers . . .

"You will do even more than I ask." [PHILEMON 21]

One of the most practical expressions of friendship toward my friend Barbara while recovering was the practical help of Jim and Phyllis, who regularly vacuumed the floor, prepared the meals, and washed the dishes. Although I was sleeping on a flip bed at the foot of Barbara's bed at night, and helping with "odds and ends" during the day, these friends would call ahead before coming over with a *"What do you need us to bring?"*

Inevitably, there were always a few small items like milk and liquid detergent. Jim and Phyllis came over almost every evening for several weeks following surgery to help do whatever needed to be done—even putting up pictures. Their presence was a true expression of Christian love.

Communicate Your Care with Cards

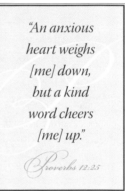

During the first few months following my diagnosis, hardly a day went by that I did not receive a note or card of encouragement. The wonderful words and special Scriptures still bring comfort to my heart ... comfort beyond imagination.

From colorful cards with stickers to decorative hand-drawn letters, I clearly see that creativity knows no bounds. Each letter—some from people whom I don't even know—is meaningful. Each piece of correspondence is cherished because someone took personal time to write.

> *"An anxious heart weighs [me] down, but a kind word cheers [me] up."*
>
> *Proverbs 12:25*

Beside my bed was a big basket of notes, letters, and cards, for at times when my heart would be down, these notes quickly cheered me up. Today I'm much more aware that ...

"An anxious heart weighs [me] down, but a kind word cheers [me] up." [PROVERBS 12:25]

Can personal messages from people we don't know have any real ministry? Oh, yes! The following letter from twenty-year-old Teresa in Fargo, North Dakota, blessed me beyond measure:

"I think of you and how much you mean to my heart, and I imagine there must be at least 1,000,000 others that feel the same way. Especially when you start your chemo, always remember that you don't have to do this alone. There's a reason why God created others, and everybody needs an

opportunity to serve someone else . . . and soon enough you may very well be the one to give others that chance.

"My grandma, seventy-eight, also has cancer, and it has almost completely taken over her earthly body. She's what one would call a 'living saint.' I visited her about a week ago, and she had come to the point where she was really down. I asked her how it felt being so close to the one goal she's had all her life: seeing Jesus face-to-face. She said, 'I'm really excited, and I have a great peace.' So then I said, 'Then why the long face?' Her servant-of-servants heart replied that she's not doing much to serve the Lord. Physically speaking, she's unable to serve the Lord.

"Then I brought to her mind how she's helping others by allowing others to visit her, clothe her, feed her . . . all those super humbling things. She's helping them to be more like Jesus . . . because that's what HE would have done. She seemed to glow in the dark after the realization of that."

Teresa's sentiments ministered to my soul! Her letter helped me change my perspective to more readily allow others to give to me without my feeling that I was imposing. I needed that change of perspective.

". . . Encourage one another daily . . . ." [HEBREWS 3:13]

Be Prepared to Help for the Long Haul

48

It is not unusual for visits, calls, and offers of help to taper off after a couple weeks. When someone calls and a cheery voice answers, the assumption can be made that all is well and help is no longer needed. However, this is sometimes far from the truth.

Even when spirits are high and recovery is going well, it doesn't mean that needs are no longer present, especially when a loved one is undergoing chemo or radiation treatments and energy is low. The side effects of these treatments can render anyone incapable of performing simple tasks that are suddenly too strenuous to accomplish.

Be committed to being available for the long haul and to continue helping throughout the length of the cancer treatments. Such perseverance and faithfulness will be forever remembered and deeply appreciated.

"It is not unusual for visits, calls, and offers of help to taper off after a couple weeks. Be committed to being available for the long haul."

June

"Love . . . always hopes, always perseveres."
[1 CORINTHIANS 13:7]

49

Accompany Your Loved One to Chemo

After several months of chemotherapy, I called my dear friend who had been fighting cancer for several years. *"Sue, please forgive me for being so insensitive."* *"There's nothing you've done to forgive,"* she responded.

"Oh yes, there is." I protested. *"Tell me, what could I have done for you that would have been truly meaningful?"* *"Oh June, you didn't need to do anything."*

"No, Sue. Tell me. What would have really been meaningful?" Again she deflected my questions. *"I didn't want to take you away from the important work you are doing,"* she assured me.

"No, I really want to know," I insisted. *"Well . . ."* she hesitated, then softly answered, *"I wish you had come with me just once for chemotherapy."*

Of course! How easy that would have been. But I didn't know. Yet at the same time, I realize how comforting it was for me to have understanding friends and family during those times of my own treatment. But, Sue's words helped me to have focus.

A few weeks later another friend was scheduled for her

first chemo treatment. I'll never forget the look of surprise and joy on Muriel's face when I walked in and sat with her for an hour as she embarked on her new, uncertain journey. If I had not traveled this same path, I wouldn't have known how to be sensitive to her need.

I can sincerely say that what others have looked upon as "bad" has been truly used for good in my life. And I pray that God will continue to use my chemo experience to help me to be sensitive and to reach out to the needs of others.

My friend Sue has since gone home to be with the Lord, and although I miss her terribly at times, I am grateful that her long, hard-fought battle with cancer is over and that she is now literally walking with her Lord and enjoying the place He had prepared specifically for her. I am also grateful that her life is still impacting my life and the lives of others.

"I can sincerely say that what others have looked upon as 'bad' has been truly used for good in my life."

June

Sue was one of my "fun" forever friends. I love to think of her with her head back, eyes sparkling, and peals of laughter coming from her mouth. She was one of God's special blessings. He had a special call on her life, and because of her life He is still working . . . for my good and for the good of others.

"We know that in all things God works for the good of those who love him, who have been called according to his purpose." [ROMANS 8:28]

Don't Forget
about
the Children

Don't Forget about the Children!

When a father or mother has a life-threatening illness, often the stress is so great and the grief so deep that children get lost in the shuffle. Because life has taken a dramatic turn for the parents, another adult may need to come alongside to help the children make the turn also.

Perhaps the greatest gift you can give to a parent struggling with a serious illness is choosing to focus on the children: learn their likes and dislikes . . . notice their needs . . . help them face their fears. Consider these possible suggestions . . .

- When visiting your friend, be a friend to the children. Spend time talking with each child, if possible, one-on-one. Begin with general questions such as, "What do you like most about school?" "Who is your favorite teacher . . . and why?" "How is this year different from last year?"

- Bring a batch of home baked cookies for them to put in their lunch box . . . or enough for them to share with their friends. Better yet, give the goodies to their mother to give to the children. This helps Mom still feel like a mom!

- Be aware of Christmas and birthday gifts. Ask your friend, "Would you like for me to buy something special for you to give to Jimmy?" (If so, buy the gift-wrap as well, but let your friend see the gift before it's wrapped.)

- Purchase humorous cards, posters, or gifts for your loved one to give. Although this is a "heavy" time, these fun items allow the sick one to introduce some much needed levity. Remember, children love to laugh.

- Carry a camera when you visit. Take pictures of the children, both by themselves as well as with their parents. Put exceptional pictures in a frame. Even though most of the attention is on the one who is ill, this special attention lets the kids know that they are still important.

- Does a child need extra transportation for a field trip or to a birthday party? Volunteer to be the chauffeur for a special event. Be sure to inquire ahead of time about what the child is to bring.

- After the treatment has become routine, offer to take the children to observe the chemo treatment for a little while. Doing so may take away the mystique and answer many questions they may have about this part of the therapy. It would also allow them to be a part of the process with their family member.

- Offer to take the children to buy school supplies or school clothes or a special outfit for no particular occasion. One grown daughter continues year after year to thank me for taking her (along with her brother and sisters) to buy clothes during a time when their mother was physically incapacitated. I'm still absolutely amazed at the long-term impact this one act of kindness has had through the years.

Amidst the maze of emotions, the children need to be assured that they aren't suddenly less loved and their welfare isn't less important. A parent's severe illness is a clear case of a family in crisis ... and you can help the family by focusing on the children.

Will these and other little acts of kindness make any real difference? Yes, beyond a shadow of doubt! The greatest treasures in God's kingdom are built from the smallest acts of kindness toward His little ones. A truly unselfish gift is one that is given to one who cannot return the favor. And, in the eyes of the Lord, any act of kindness toward someone in need is an act of love toward Him. Jesus said,

"For I was hungry and you gave Me food; I was thirsty and you gave Me drink; I was a stranger and you took Me in; I was naked and you clothed Me; I was sick and you visited Me . . . . 'Lord, when did we see You hungry and feed You, or thirsty and give You drink? When did we see You a stranger and take You in, or naked and clothe You?' . . . Inasmuch as you did it to one of the least of these My brethren, you did it to Me."
[MATTHEW 25:35 – 40 NKJV]

Questions to Help Children

Questions to Help Children

Preserving life takes precedence over everyone and everything else. But if the real needs of the children are not met, they can feel cut off from their parents, confused about God, and unconnected with life as they have known it. Asking key questions, showing real interest, and talking "heart-to-heart" can help turn children in the direction they need to go.

- "What do you know about Mommy's illness?"

- "Do you know what caused Daddy's cancer?"

- "Do you know that you've not done or said anything that has caused Mommy's sickness?"

- "What would you like to do for Daddy to express your love for him?"

- "Are you afraid you too may become sick?"

- "Are there some questions you have about what the doctors are doing to make Mommy well?"

- "Do you know it is okay to feel frustrated because Daddy is so sick and unable to do things with you like he used to?"

- "Would you like to go to the doctor's office with Mommy sometime so you can see what she does down there?"

- "Do you know that there's still no one in the world that Mommy and Daddy love more than you? You will always be special in their hearts."

- "What do you do when you feel sad about Daddy's illness?"

- "Would you like for us to pray together and ask Jesus to take care of Mommy, to comfort and encourage her, and to let her know how much you love her?"

- "Could we pray together and thank Jesus for taking care of you, asking Him to also comfort and encourage you?"

- "Do you know that Mommy and Daddy will always love you and will make sure that you are always taken care of?"

- "What things have changed for you since Mommy has been sick?"

- "What are some things you and I can do to make Daddy feel better?"

- "What do you think about your Mommy's illness?"

- "What are some of the things you think about or worry about?"

- "Do you know about the things your Daddy is doing to try to get better?"

- "Would you like for us to think of some special things you could do for your mother, like reading her favorite Scriptures or something from a book to her. or writing thank-you notes for her?"

  "The tongue of the wise brings healing." [PROVERBS 12:18]

Tips for Temporary Trials

Tips for Temporary Trials

No person gives better driving directions than a driver who has already gone where you need to go. Likewise, no person gives better advice on a trial than someone who has persevered in that trial. In the midst of the trials of cancer treatment, the counsel of one who has gone before is an invaluable gift worth its weight in gold. The list below reflects practical wisdom from caring people who preceded me in tackling their trials.

"The lips of the wise spread knowledge." [PROVERBS 15:7]

Before Beginning Treatments[13]

• Tell your doctor what medications (prescription and over-the-counter), vitamins, and the like that you are taking and whether you have any allergies. Some medications, herbs, and vitamins can interfere with the effectiveness of treatments.

• Obtain a complete dental/oral checkup.

Before Each Treatment

• Eat solid food—but only nibble, nibble, nibble on the day of chemo and one to two days afterward so as not to overextend the stomach.

After Each Treatment

• Drink plenty of liquids to flush the chemicals out of your body: water (preferably filtered or spring water), fruit juices, lemonade, ginger ale, and club soda.

- Frozen fruit bars and ice cubes help to put fluids into your body. Avoid caffeine and alcohol because both cause dehydration.

Aching Bones/Joints

- Calcium tablets (a minimum of 1,200–1,500 mg.) are essential because chemotherapy assaults the bone marrow most severely.

- Nonsteroidal anti-inflammatory drugs can be purchased over the counter and can be helpful in controlling or relieving pain.

- If necessary, take prescription medication for discomfort as your physician recommends.

Anemia (low red blood cell count)

- Eat red meat and liver, beets, and green vegetables (especially spinach and broccoli, dark green leafy salads — not iceberg lettuce, which has little nutritional value and is very hard to digest).

- Some say that one tablespoon daily of unsulfured blackstrap molasses was the answer to their low red blood cell count.

- With the consent of your physician, consider taking nutritional supplements that can help build your blood count. Many physicians know the value of sublingual B–12 or B–12 injections. Chlorophyll in a liquid or a capsule often builds the blood quite well.

Antioxidant Foods (cancer fighters)

- Fruits: Apples, berries, cantaloupe, cherries, grapes, oranges, and plums all help fight cancer. Berries also protect the

DNA from damage. Cherries contain *anthocyanins.*

- Nuts: Raw almonds contain laetrile, which is thought by many to be a good cancer fighter.

- Vegetables: The cabbage family, called "cruciferous," contains more anticancer properties than any other group — cabbage, broccoli, Brussels sprouts, cauliflower, horseradish, mustard greens, radishes, rutabaga, turnips, and watercress.

- Carrots and carrot juice are a source of *beta-carotene.*

- Green vegetables contain *chlorophyll,* another cancer fighter.

- Mushrooms and legumes (including chick peas, lentils, and red beans).

- Onions and garlic enhance the immune system. Garlic is a natural antibiotic.

Constipation

- Eat prunes, bran, wheat, and rye bread, and other fiber products.

- Drink prune juice, water, and other liquids. Hot prune juice is especially helpful.

Diarrhea[14]

- Avoid *high fiber* food or other foods that cause cramps or gas, such as raw fruits and vegetables, caffeine, beans, cabbage, whole-grain breads, cereals, lactose-based dairy products, sweets, and spicy foods.

- Eat *low fiber* foods like bananas, potatoes, and apricots, which are also high in potassium.

- Over-the-counter, natural, dietary fiber supplements can help stop diarrhea.

- Drink clear liquids, including weak tea, broth, apple juice, and soup to avoid dehydration.

- Electrolytes and hydration lost through diarrhea can be replenished with certain over-the-counter drinks (some are suitable for children). At least one comes as a frozen bar, which provides variety.

- Acidophilus capsules and yogurt with live cultures help replenish the loss of good bacteria.

- Keep an over-the-counter antidiarrheal medication nearby or carry it with you.

Dry/Cracked Skin

- Cod liver oil capsules replenish oils throughout the body (up to four capsules a day).

- If you are troubled by dry skin, a good moisturizing cream rich with emollients may give comfort.

- Dry, chapped hands can be helped by liberally applying a therapeutic hand cream and covering the hands with cotton gloves to hold the moisture in.

Dry Eyes

- Eye drops of saline solution can be carried wherever you go.

Energy Loss

- The two fastest sources of energy are orange juice and honey.

- Since energy begets energy, do some aerobic exercise like vigorous walking, swimming, or biking every day (or at least four times a week). Exercise promotes oxygenation of the tissues.

Fingernail Splitting

• Eat Jell-O and other gelatin products.

• Clear nail polish to a limited degree helps keep the nail intact.

• Avoid polish remover containing acetone or alcohol, which is very drying to nails and skin.

Hair Loss (alopecia)[15]

• Patients who are prescribed certain chemotherapy drugs inevitably experience hair loss. Hair "releases" from the scalp between days 14 to 17. When chemo stops, hair growth starts.

• Initially, hair grows back with a different texture (usually baby fine), a different thickness (usually thinner), and a different shape (usually curly). Hair may even grow back a different color. (Blondes, this could be your chance to become brunettes!)

• Hair even grows back at different speeds on different parts of the head (faster in the back, slower in the front). So, be patient, patient, patient. Usually six months after chemotherapy ends, you will have grown about three inches of hair. Following chemotherapy, hair takes longer to grow than normal, and it may not return as it once was. (Just make the best of having some of those "bad hair days.")

Hot Flashes

• Dress in layers.

• Avoid caffeine and alcohol.

• Exercise.

• Be aware that spicy foods exacerbate hot flashes.

Lymphedema

• Lymphedema (a condition of excessive swelling) may affect up to 10% of those who have auxiliary lymph nodes removed.

• Lifting or carrying heavy items can cause swelling. (Have grocery bags loaded lightly.)

• Have blood taken, injections given, and blood pressure measured from the unaffected arm and hand.

• Because cuts and abrasions take much longer to heal, avoid any type of injury to the hand, arm, or underarm. Use an electric razor instead of a blade to shave underarms. Wear gloves while gardening to avoid puncture wounds.

• When flying in an airplane, wear a pressure glove and a pressure sleeve to keep swelling to a minimum.

• Massaging the swollen area is very effective.

Mouth Dryness[16]

• Sip cool water throughout the day, suck ice chips, and eat frozen fruit bars.

• Suck on sugar-free hard candy or chew sugar-free gum.

• Avoid tobacco and alcoholic drinks, for they cause dryness.

• Moisten food with butter, broth, gravies, and sauces.

• Use lip balm for dry lips.

• Ask your doctor about products that either replace or stimulate your own saliva.

Mouth Sores (stomatitis)[17]

- Avoid acidic foods (tomatoes, citrus fruit, and fruit juice), which can cause mouth and throat irritation. Avoid spices and coarse foods, such as raw vegetables, dry crackers, and granola.

- Eat soft foods that are easy to swallow, such as eggs, cooked cereal, soft fruit (bananas and apple sauce), soup, mashed potatoes, cottage cheese, macaroni and cheese, ice cream, custard, and yogurt with live cultures.

- Change the consistency of foods by adding fluids and using soups, sauces, and gravies to make them softer.

- Cut your food into small, bite-sized pieces and chew longer than usual.

- Puree your food, or drink liquid food supplements.

- Avoid hot beverages. Cold beverages are soothing to the mouth. Put wet washcloths inside plastic zip bags and keep them in the freezer. Later apply to the sore mouth.

- Brush teeth lightly with an extra-soft toothbrush using a fluoride toothpaste containing no abrasives. Avoid using dental floss. (If you feel you must, floss gently with waxed, non-shredding floss.)

- Rinse your mouth gently and frequently with a solution made of 1/2 teaspoon baking soda and 1/2 teaspoon salt in a large glass of warm water, especially after you brush. Follow with a plain water rinse.

- Use only an alcohol-free mouthwash. (Alcohol has a drying effect on the mouth tissues.) Prescription mouthwashes may provide significant relief.

- When taking pills, if the normal drinking water feels irritating in your mouth (it did for me), use lightly salted liquids, such as chicken or beef broth. (Sometimes I even added a little salt to my drinking water.)

- Acidophilus capsules can have an antibacterial effect on the body. (I took four capsules that contain acidophilus and goat's milk several times a day—and no, you don't taste the goat's milk—it's inside the capsule!)

Nausea[18]

- Eat small, frequent amounts of bland food: dry toast, crackers, gelatin, salty chips, ramen noodle soup, ginger snaps and other ginger products, cold dill or sour pickles, carbonated drinks, high carbohydrate foods, oatmeal, potatoes, rice, wheat toast, spaghetti, macaroni and cheese, and other pasta dishes.

- Avoid fried or high fat foods and foods with a strong aroma.

- Drink cold water or suck on ice chips between meals.

- Eat a light meal one or two hours before and after your treatment, eating and drinking slowly.

- Prepare for the trip home from the chemo treatments with some very helpful items: a plastic basin or pan for nausea, wet washcloths in plastic zip bags, a roll of paper towels, a box of facial tissues, some crushed ice in a cooler to help with nausea, a cup and a spoon, ginger ale, a bottle of water, and a pillow.

- Consult your physician about using suppositories and/or oral medications for nausea, including an antiemetic to prevent nausea prior to treatment.

Nosebleeds

• Cod liver oil capsules replenish oils in the tissues of your skin.

• Sleep with a cool mist humidifier (not warm) close to your bed.

• Cold washcloths to the nose will help stop the bleeding.

Platelet Loss

• Expect to bruise easily until the platelet count is restored to your normal range. (Platelets are those particles that plug up little holes in our blood systems so that we don't ooze blood all the time. Excessive loss of platelets can lead to excessive bleeding or "free bleeding.")

• Although rare, in order to protect yourself from internal bleeding, you may need one or more platelet transfusions to replace this needed element in your blood. (I had two transfusions.)

• Protect yourself from any possible skin cuts, scrapes, or pricks because external bleeding may be difficult to stop. (Avoid activities with sharp objects like needles, razors, knives, and thorny plants.)

• If you have a cold, blow gently into a soft tissue.

• Wear long sleeves to help protect the skin.

• Do not take pain relievers (aspirin, ibuprofen, etc.) without first consulting your doctor. These medications can weaken the platelets and cause excessive bleeding.

Swelling

- Avoid salty foods.

- Keep legs and feet elevated above your heart when sitting and, if necessary, when sleeping.

- For excessive swelling of the legs, ask your physician about wearing pressure hose.

- Some prescription diuretics are potassium-depleting while others are not. Your doctor may decide it is necessary for you to take a potassium supplement in order to keep the electrolytes in your heart functioning properly.

Toenail Fungus and Detaching

- Trim each affected toenail to conform to the toe, and then forget about it. Following chemotherapy, your toenails usually grow back.

- Soak feet in Epsom salts if nails loosen or drain.

- Be patient, regrowth will take a number of months.

Weight Gain

- Know that gaining weight is temporary because of fluid buildup. Your metabolism may also be "out of commission" because of chemo.

- Losing weight will be easier after chemo when steroids are no longer in the medications. Continue to walk briskly or do any other aerobic exercises to increase your metabolism.

White Cell Count Loss (leukopenia)

- Your doctor may treat you with specific medications for a loss of white cells in the blood. Repeated injections help rebuild bone marrow, which is essential, because bone marrow produces the white cells necessary to fight infection.

If the white cell blood count drops excessively low, you may need to be hospitalized and be given antibiotics until the medication takes effect.

Call your doctor when symptoms occur. Many side effects can be treated; however, not calling can allow them to worsen. You must keep in mind that you're not "bothering" the doctor or nurse! Remember, ***if you have a temperature of 100.5 or greater, call your doctor or nurse, day or night.***

Red Blood Cell Count Loss

*   You may develop anemia during chemotherapy. Symptoms include fatigue, shortness of breath, and dizziness. Your doctor can prescribe something that will help rebuild your blood count and thus relieve the uncomfortable symptoms.

Discover the Important Don'ts

Discover the Important Don'ts

As I progressed through my cancer treatment, I developed an acute awareness of "the little things"—like every little thing I put in my mouth! Suddenly everything became suspect as I sought to be wise and cancer-minded in all I ate, even down to the vitamins I took on a daily basis. And if I even thought about cheating, Kay or one of my other watchdog friends was looking over my shoulder to keep me on the straight and narrow. I quickly learned some valuable don'ts for anyone determined to develop new healthy habits in the midst of the cancer ordeal.

Don't be ignorant about Vitamin C.

This was one of my biggest surprises. At the onset of the chemotherapy treatments, my oncologist, Dr. Joyce O'Shaughnessy, asked me to bring a list of all vitamins and medications I was currently taking. She also wanted me to consult with her before I took anything that caring people would send or suggest.

Imagine my surprise when Dr. O. immediately—and permanently—deleted from my stash of pills the daily dose of 1000 mg. of time-release vitamin C that I had taken for years. Immediately I asked, "Why should I eliminate this vitamin, which is known for its antioxidant, cell protection effects?" She explained that current research reveals that vitamin C can *prevent* the development of cancer, but other studies indicate that vitamin C can *promote* the growth of early cancers. Because of this uncertainty, many oncologists recommend avoiding supplemental vitamin C. A normal diet and a regular multivitamin should be enough.

Don't assume that soy milk is OK.

Consult your doctor before using soy milk. Researchers continue to explore whether the estrogen in soy milk might either stimulate breast cancer or interfere with the benefit of one of the prescriptions if the cancer is "estrogen receptor positive." Most oncologists do not recommend dieting or taking supplements high in soy with estrogen receptor positive cancer.

Don't consume alcohol.

The American Cancer Society reports that having two to five drinks a day increases the risk of cancer recurring by 50%. "Alcohol consumption is an established cause of cancers of the mouth, pharynx, larynx, esophagus, liver, and breast. For each of these cancers, risk increases substantially with intake of more than two drinks per day. Regular consumption of even a few drinks per week has been associated with an increased risk of breast cancer in women."[19]

Don't be in denial about the impact of sugar.

Many resources say that sugar feeds cancer.

Don't be uninformed about HRT.

"Hormone Replacement Therapy" (HRT) has its definite advantages, most notably, protection against osteoporosis and relief from hot flashes. However, doctors usually counsel individuals to weigh the benefits of hormone replacement (estrogen, progestin) against the risks of developing cancer. If hormones are used, they usually recommend the lowest dose to achieve the desired goals.[20]

Bottom line: Talk to the doctor about the *don'ts*. As you read, study, share information with one another, and talk with your doctors, you will know how to be prudent and avoid the danger zones. The Bible gives this caution ...

"The prudent see danger and take refuge, but the simple keep going and suffer for it." [PROVERBS 27:12]

What Cancer Cannot Do

What Cancer Cannot Do

What Cancer Cannot Do

*It cannot lessen **love**.*

*It cannot fracture **faith**.*

*It cannot hinder **hope**.*

*It cannot prevent **peace**.*

*It cannot crush **confidence**.*

*It cannot kill **friendship**.*

*It cannot keep out **memories**.*

*It cannot corrode **courage**.*

*It cannot shatter the **soul**.*

*It cannot quench the **spirit**.*

*It cannot stop resurrection **power**.*

*It cannot erode **eternal life**.*

— Author Unknown

Adapted by June Hunt

Do You Need Spiritual Healing?

Do You Need Spiritual Healing?

When a person hears the diagnosis, *"You have cancer,"* the immediate reaction is basically, *"What can I do . . . physically?"* Because every person has a body and a spirit, often another significant question is, *"What can I do . . . spiritually?"*

Based on the Bible, you should recognize that your present body is temporal, awaiting the resurrection when it will be changed—*"Listen, I tell you a mystery: We will not all sleep, but we will all be changed"* [1 CORINTHIANS 15:51]. (See also First THESSALONIANS 4:13–18.]—but your spirit is eternal ... *"While they were stoning him. Stephen prayed, 'Lord Jesus, receive my spirit'"* [ACTS 7:59]. This present body is destined to die, but the spirit will exist *either* forever with God or forever away from God. (The first is spiritual life; the second is spiritual death.) So what do you need to know to have spiritual life?

How to Have Spiritual Life

- ***Recognize there is a problem.***

  Let's assume your body is terminally ill as a result of cancer. What would happen if a healthy man could and would exchange his healthy body for your cancerous body? Physically, he would die and you would live! Likewise, assume your spirit is terminally ill due to being imperfect (what the Bible calls "sinful"). EZEKIEL 18:4 says, *"The soul who sins is the one who will die."*... And the truth is, we've all sinned. As a result *"Your iniquities [sins] have separated you from your God"* [ISAIAH 59:2]. But what would happen if a perfect man could and would exchange his perfection for your imperfection? Spiritually, he would die and you would live.

- **God took the initiative to solve the problem.**

   In reality, Jesus took the penalty for your sins by dying in your place so that you could receive His full forgiveness and live forever with God. The Bible explains, *"God demonstrates his own love for us in this: While we were still sinners, Christ died for us"* [ROMANS 5:8]. He willingly offers you this great exchange—His death for your life.

- **You have a part in the solution.**

   In order to receive this forgiveness, you must humble your heart, be willing to confess your sins, and turn from them. The Bible reveals, *"If we confess our sins, he is faithful and just and will forgive us our sins and purify us from all unrighteousness"* [1 JOHN 1:9].

- **You have a decision to make.**

   If you receive Jesus as your personal Savior and Lord—giving Him total control of your life—He will forgive all your sins and give you eternal life. The Bible declares this good news: *"God so loved the world that he gave his one and only Son, that whoever believes in him shall not perish but have eternal life"* [JOHN 3:16].

- **God offers you a great gift.**

   Assume that you become ill in a foreign country and desperately need medicine that your money can't buy. All of a sudden, you hear that a gift has been offered to you—not aspirin, not cough medicine, but the only medicine that could cure your disease. For the medicine to be effective, you would need to receive it and take it. Salvation is like that. You need to receive God's gift to you with faith and apply it to your life. God says that your salvation is based on your faith in (entrusting your life to) Jesus Christ alone. Jesus said, *"I am the way and the truth and the life. No one comes to the Father except through me"* [JOHN 14:6].

If you want to become spiritually alive and whole, you can receive this new life now by sincerely praying this prayer to God.

My Prayer

"God, I admit that I am not perfect and that I have sinned. Many times I have gone my own way instead of Your way. Please forgive me for all my sins. Thank You, Jesus, for dying on the cross to pay the penalty for my sins. Come into my life to be my Lord and Savior. Take control of my life and make me the person You want me to be. Thank You, Jesus, for what You will do in me, to me, and through me. In Jesus name I pray. Amen."

ENDNOTES

1. Used by permission.

2. Crunch © Nestlé, 2005; Snickers © Mars, 2005; Butterfinger © Nestlé, 2005; Air Heads © Perfetti Van Melle, 2001–2003.

3. American Cancer Society, *Cancer Facts and Figures 2005* (Atlanta, GA: American Cancer Society, 2005), 1.

4. Michael Retsky, "Cancer Growth: Implications for Medicine and Malpractice," Technical Assistance Bureau, Inc., <http://www.tabexperts.com/CancerGrowth.htm>.

5. For breast cancer tumor classifications, see American Cancer Society and National Comprehensive Cancer Network, *Breast Cancer: Treatment Guidelines for Patients,* version 5, July 2003 (Atlanta, GA: American Cancer Society, 2003), 13.

6. For cancer stages, see American Cancer Society and National Comprehensive Cancer Network, *Breast Cancer: Treatment Guidelines for Patients,* 14.

7. American Cancer Society, *Cancer Facts and Figures 2005,* 9.

8. For the chemotherapy process, see American Cancer Society and National Comprehensive Cancer Network, *Breast Cancer: Treatment Guidelines for Patients,* 19–25.

9. For the radiation therapy process, see American Cancer Society and National Comprehensive Cancer Network, *Breast Cancer: Treatment Guidelines for Patients,* 17–18; National Institutes of Health Department of Health and Human Services, National Cancer Institute, *Radiation Therapy and You: A Guide to Self-help During Cancer Treatment* (Bethesda, MD: National Cancer Institute, 2003), 5.

10. For the hormone therapy process, see American Cancer Society and National Comprehensive Cancer Network, *Breast Cancer: Treatment Guidelines for Patients,* 21.

11. Used by permission.

12. Joanna Cooke, "Lymphedema after Breast Cancer," 2002, Breast Cancer Action Kingston <http://www.brcanactionkingston.com/lymph.html>.

13. For information regarding beginning your treatment see National Institutes of Health Department of Health and Human Services, National Cancer Institute, *Radiation Therapy and You: A Guide to Self-help During Cancer Treatment,* 18, 36.

14. For information regarding avoiding diarrhea with radiation therapy, see National Institutes of Health Department of Health and Human Services, National Cancer Institute, *Radiation Therapy and You: A Guide to Self-help During Cancer Treatment,* 42.

15. For information regarding hair loss and radiation therapy, see National Institutes of Health Department of Health and Human Services, National Cancer Institute, Radiation Therapy and You: A Guide to Self-help During Cancer Treatment, 31.

16. For information regarding mouth dryness and radiation therapy, see National Institutes of Health Department of Health and Human Services, National Cancer Institute, *Radiation Therapy and You: A Guide to Self-help During Cancer Treatment,* 38.

17. For information regarding mouth sores and radiation therapy, see National Institutes of Health Department of Health and Human Services, National Cancer Institute, *Radiation Therapy and You: A Guide to Self-help During Cancer Treatment,* 36–37.

18. For information regarding nausea and radiation therapy, see National Institutes of Health Department of Health and Human Services, National Cancer Institute, *Radiation Therapy and You: A Guide to Self-help During Cancer Treatment,* 41.

19. American Cancer Society, *Cancer Facts and Figures 2005* (Atlanta, GA: American Cancer Society, 2005), 46.

20. *Hormone Replacement Therapy and Breast Cancer Relapse.* February 5, 2005. National Cancer Institute. http://www.cancer.gov/clinicaltrials/results/hrt-and-breast-cancer0204.

Selected Bibliography

American Cancer Society. *Cancer Facts and Figures 2005*. Atlanta, GA: American Cancer Society, 2005.

American Cancer Society. "Detailed Guide: Breast Cancer: What are the Risk Factors for Breast Cancer?" 2004. American Cancer Society. http://www.cancer.org/docroot/CRI/content/CRI_2_4_2X_What_ are_the_risk_factors_for_breast_cancer_5.asp?sitearea=.

American Cancer Society and National Comprehensive Cancer Network. *Breast Cancer: Treatment Guidelines for Patients*. Version 5, July 2003. Atlanta, GA: American Cancer Society, 2003.

Cooke, Joanna. "Lymphedema after Breast Cancer." 2002. Breast Cancer Action Kingston. http://www.brcanactionkingston.com/lymph.html.

Department of Health and Human Services, National Institutes of Health, National Cancer Institute. *Radiation Therapy and You: A Guide to Self-help During Cancer Treatment*. Bethesda, MD: National Cancer Institute, 2003.

LaTour, Kathy. *The Breast Cancer Companion*. New York: Avon, 1993.

Love, Susan with Karen Lindsey. *Dr. Susan Love's Breast Book*. Illustrated by Marcia Williams. 3d ed. Cambridge: Perseus, 2000.

Quillin, Patrick with Noreen Quillin. *Beating Cancer with Nutrition*. Rev. ed. Carlsbad, CA: Nutrition Times, 2001.

Retsky, Michael. "Cancer Growth: Implications for Medicine and Malpractice." Technical Assistance Bureau, Inc. http://www.tabexperts. com/CancerGrowth.htm.

Providing God's Truth for Today's Problems

BIBLICAL COUNSELING KEYS . . .

are "people helper" resources based
on the fundamental truths of the Bible.

TOPICS AVAILABLE

Abortion Prevention

Adoption

Adultery

Aging

Alcohol & Drug Abuse

Anger

Anorexia & Bulimia

Assurance of Salvation

Atheism & Agnosticism

The Bible

Blended Family

Caregiving

Child Evangelism

Childhood Sexual Abuse

Chronic Illness/Disabilities

Codependency

Communication

Conflict Resolution

Confrontation

Counseling

Critical Spirit

Cults

Dating

Death

Decision Making

Depression

Divorce

Dysfunctional Family

Employment

Envy & Jealousy

Ethics & Integrity

Euthanasia

Evil & Suffering . . . Why?

Fear

Financial Freedom

Forgiveness

Friendship

God: Who is He?

Grief Recovery

Guilt

Habits

Holy Spirit

Homosexuality

Hope

Identity: Who Are You?

Infertility

Intimacy

Islam

Jehovah's Witnesses

Jesus, Is He God?

Jewish Fulfillment

Loneliness

Lying

Manipulation

Marriage

Mentoring

Midlife Crisis

Mormonism

New Age Spirituality

The Occult

Overeating

Parenting

Perfectionism

Pregnancy... Unplanned

Prejudice

Premarital Counseling

Pride & Humility

Procrastination

Prosperity

Purpose in Life

Rape Recovery

Rebellion

Reconciliation

Rejection

Salvation

Satan, Demons & Satanism

Self-worth

Sexual Addiction

Sexual Integrity

Single Parenting

Singleness

Spiritual Abuse & Legalism

Spiritual Warfare

Stealing

Stress Management

Submission

Success through Failure

Suicide Prevention

Teenagers

Temptation

Terminal Illness

Time Management

Trials

Unbelieving Mate

Verbal & Emotional Abuse

Victimization

Widowhood

Wife Abuse

Workaholism

Worry

All the resources offered by HOPE FOR THE HEART are drawn from the heart of God's Word. We believe the Bible is the only standard by which trustworthy counsel should be measured.

MINI-BOOKS BY JUNE HUNT

Hope & Healing from Adultery

Hope for Alcohol & Drug Abuse

God's Heart on Atheism & Agnosticism

God's Heart on Childhood Sexual Abuse

God's Heart on Cults

Hope & Healing from Depression

God's Heart on Decision Making

God's Heart on Guilt

God's Heart on The Holy Spirit

God's Heart on Homosexuality

God's Heart on Jewish Fulfillment

God's Heart on Mormonism

God's Heart on The Occult

God's Heart on Parenting

God's Heart on Pregnancy ... Unplanned

God's Heart on Premarital Counseling

Hope & Help for Sexual Addiction

God's Heart on Sexual Integrity

God's Heart on Spiritual Warfare

God's Heart on Teenagers

God's Heart on Verbal & Emotional Abuse

God's Heart on Victimization

Hope & Healing from Wife Abuse

OTHER BOOKS BY JUNE HUNT

Bonding with Your Teen through Boundaries

Healing the Hurting Heart

Seeing Yourself Through God's Eyes

WHAT CAN YOU DO THAT WILL MAKE A REAL DIFFERENCE?

Some of us are "all thumbs" when it comes to comforting others who face a difficult illness! It's hard to find just the right words to say or just the right thing to do that will show how much you sincerely care.

Conquering the Challenge of Cancer includes:

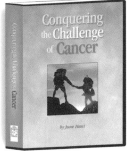

- **Book:** *Caring For a Loved One With Cancer,* a personal history of how June's own friends and family came to her rescue in many simple but practical ways.

- **Four audio CDs:** Walk with June through her personal experience after hearing the dreaded word . . . cancer!

Where do you find answers?
What do you do next?
What kind of treatment is best for you?

Disc 1 — June's Journey: Courage in the Midst of Cancer

Disc 2 — The Cancer Journey with Faith, Hope and Love

Disc 3 — Caring for a Loved One with Cancer, Part I

Disc 4 — Caring for a Loved One with Cancer, Part II

Discover how you too can make a real difference in the life of another!

To order or ask about other resources available on this topic, call

1.800.488.HOPE (4673)

Please visit our website at
www.hopefortheheart.org
for a complete listing of our Biblically-based
counseling resources.

HERE'S HOW TO ORDER . . .

By Phone
1.800.488.HOPE (4673)

By Fax
972.239.0122

By Mail
HOPE FOR THE HEART
P.O. Box 7
Dallas, TX 75221

On the Internet
www.hopefortheheart.org

For further product information and other inquiries,
please call:
1.800.488 HOPE (4673) or
972.239.9999 in the Dallas area.

HELP US HELP YOU!

Thank you for taking the time to read this book. Your opinion is important to us, and we need your candid thoughts. Please take a few minutes to complete this questionnaire. You are the reason we are here. Be honest and frank—these results will shape our future. We greatly appreciate your willingness to support Hope For The Heart with your sincere response and thoughtful ideas.

Please Return to:
HOPE FOR THE HEART
Attn: Reader Response
P.O. Box 7
Dallas, TX 75221

CHANGED MINDS

CHANGED HEARTS

CHANGED LIVES!

CARING FOR A LOVED ONE WITH CANCER

Do you feel this book was helpful? ☐ Yes ☐ No

*If not, what would make it more helpful?*_____
_____
_____

What one change would you make? _____
_____
_____

What other topics are of interest to you? _____
_____
_____

I would like more information on: _____
_____
_____

I would like to share my testimony or the greatest benefit I received from this book:

_____

_____

_____

_____

_____

_____

_____

_____

_____

_____

_____

_____

_____

_____

_____

_____

_____

_____

_____

_____

_____

_____

_____

_____

_____

_____

_____

You may publish my testimony.

Anonymous _____

Initial, Last name _____

City, state _____

Please do not use my testimony for publication.

Name: _____

Address: _____

E-mail: _____

My Notes

My Notes

My Notes

My Notes